230

D0210168

B
Q

DAVID GUTERSON

The Drowned Son

A BLOOMSBURY QUID

This story first appeared in
Harper's Magazine, February 1996
First published in Great Britain 1996

Copyright © 1996 by David Guterson

The moral right of the author has been asserted

Bloomsbury Publishing Plc,
2 Soho Square, London W1V 6HB

A CIP catalogue record for this book
is available from the British Library

ISBN 0 7475 2893 4

Typeset by Hewer Text Composition Services,
Edinburgh
Printed by St Edmundsbury Press, Suffolk
Jacket design by Jeff Fisher

Hutchinson's son died in October. He and another man aboard the gill-netter *Fearless* went down in sixty-five-knot winds at a place known as Cape Fox. The other man lived, but Paul had died; he was lost at sea, permanently missing beneath the waves. The news came to Hutchinson and his wife in the form of a phone call, followed by a fax, from the Coast Guard base in Ketchikan, Alaska.

The day the news arrived, Hutchinson had gone duck hunting and had shot his limit by eleven-thirty. While his wife was speaking to the Coast Guard chief petty officer, Hutchinson was on the road between Vantage and Ellensburg, headed westward toward the mountains and Seattle, and feeling keenly the pleasure of his existence – three greenheads and a mallard hen in the cooler behind him, his dog asleep with her head on her paws, a thermos of coffee wedged against the dashboard, the grey reaching sageland outside. While he rolled through Rye Pass and into the Ellensburg Valley his wife read the fax message half a dozen times. Later she mulled over all the picture albums, starting with Paul as a swaddled infant and working her way forward. She found many photos from hunting expeditions, and she realised she couldn't view these without bitterness. She pondered Paul holding his first duck by the neck, smiling numbly at the camera.

While his wife lingered over photo albums, Hutchinson drank coffee and watched a football game at the Sportsman's Café in Cle Elum. There were perhaps a dozen other men present – smoking, drinking, staring silently at the screen – and Hutchinson found that the sullen, hung-over atmosphere of the place dissipated the spirit opening up in him all morning. He took a booth and, with the sports section propped against a napkin dispenser, ate two eggs, hash browns, sausage, and sourdough toast spread with blackberry jam. Now, six weeks later, it was the last decent meal he could remember eating. It had sat nicely in his gut. He'd cleaned up thoroughly with cold canteen water, then driven through Snoqualmie Pass under a cool, pale sky, Tess wide awake and panting by the window, fall sunlight washing the mountainsides. The pass was clear and windy that afternoon, and Hutchinson drove through it certain it was a good thing to arrive home early on a Saturday in October: he would have ample time to get his things put away; he would draw, pluck, and roast two of his ducks.

His wife met him at the door with the news, and Hutchinson, not believing it for a moment, hurried into his house to read the death notice from the Coast Guard.

They were eating dinner. There was no such thing as dinner. Hutchinson and his wife had both stopped cooking. She lived on slices of cheese.

'You can say that,' Hutchinson was saying. 'You can accuse me of that. But I don't think it's really fair.'

He propped himself against the stove. In one hand he held a large spoon aloft and in the other he held a soup pot. His wife was at the table with a box of cornflakes in front of her.

'They say this happens,' he reminded his wife. 'Turns out true, doesn't it.'

'Maybe, maybe not,' she answered. 'But either way, it's an observation I'm not really interested in.'

'Oh,' said Hutchinson.

'Oh,' said his wife. 'Jesus.'

He didn't eat the soup. 'I'm guilty,' he told her. 'Yes, I blame myself. Say what you want. Go ahead. I blame you, too, you know. We blame each other.'

She got up. She didn't look at him. She was very much this sort of woman and he had always known that. 'What you say about me is true,' he confessed. 'But you babied him, Laura. If you hadn't babied him he wouldn't have felt like a coward. Everybody's guilty of something, you know. We both made our contributions.'

'I'm just so sick of listening to you squirm,' answered Laura. 'It isn't worth it any more.'

She left the kitchen. He ate his soup. He stood at the stove with the soup in his mouth and knew himself disposed to feel like a coward, too: it was painful and embarrassing to think on. His own father, Paul's grandfather, had been a coward. Hutchinson understood that his own heart had shaped itself in response to his father's heart. But what boy's doesn't? What man's doesn't? It did not seem to him a bad thing, in general, to be who he was. He still believed in himself. His doubts were normal.

He insisted to himself that it was her fault, in part her fault, for not concurring with him about the need to assist Paul in the evolution of his fortitude. She had long resisted this notion. The boy had been born with a wavering at the core that Hutchinson understood. It needed work, was all. It needed consistent attention, and nothing counterproductive. So she, Laura, was a part of it. She had to see that. Then they could go forward together to suffer their punishment and to move, conjoined, toward redemption.

When he heard her step coming back down the hallway he stood holding the pot again, not eating. He leaned against the stove and observed for the thousandth time that her grieving made her unattractive. He wanted to be in bed with her, unclothed, smelling the shadow between her breasts. 'I think I want you to leave,' she said. 'I can't stand the sight of you any more.'

A week before Christmas he gave her to understand over the telephone that he was entitled to see his own daughter who was home from UCLA. His wife told him the date to come for dinner and he wrote it in capital letters on his desk calendar and then sketched a red heart with an arrow through it.

'I love you,' he said. 'I want you to know that.'

'All right,' she answered. 'You love me.'

The man who had worked with Paul aboard the *Fearless* was standing in the living room with a bourbon and water when Hutchinson came over for dinner. 'I'm Bob Pomeroy,' he said, extending his hand. 'I knew your son, Paul.'

The man didn't look like a fisherman. He was neither rugged nor large. His wire-rimmed glasses sat cockeyed on his nose, the line of his chin was too delicate. How had this man survived? thought Hutchinson. He didn't have the look of a survivor. His threadbare shirt was stained with house paint, he blinked often, his lips were cracked.

They sat at the table in the dining room. Hutchinson's daughter had gained ten pounds and had changed the style of her hair: a pageboy. She wore a pastel smock with velvet tights and coolly drank a glass of white wine. Her legs crossed, her glasses on a chain against her flat chest. She was majoring, she said, in computer science and taking classes in finance.

When all the things were on the dining-room table Bob Pomeroy spoke. 'I'm glad I came,' he said.

'We are, too,' answered Hutchinson. 'We tried to get in touch with you. We – '

'I couldn't,' said Bob Pomeroy. 'I couldn't bring myself.'

'You should have, you know,' said Hutchinson. 'What was stopping you?'

Bob Pomeroy shook his head and pressed his glasses against his nose with a dry, cracked forefinger. 'It wasn't possible,' he said. 'I'm sorry.'

Hutchinson leaned toward him across the surface of the table. 'You didn't think we wanted to hear from you?' he said. 'You didn't think we wondered every day? Didn't you try to see things from our point of view? Didn't you realise what was happening?'

'Look,' answered Bob Pomeroy firmly, 'this is ugly, Mr Hutchinson. This is going to be painful. There's a lot I'm going to have to lay on you before I leave here tonight.'

He met Hutchinson's gaze then –

watery eyes behind wire-rimmed glasses – and Hutchinson sat back, his heart wavering. 'I'll tell you the whole story,' said the fisherman. 'It's like my duty to Paul to tell you everything.'

The *Fearless*, Bob explained, was primarily a salmon boat, geared to gill net or to troll, depending. Bob's habit was to run the Inside Passage from Seattle to Juneau mid-April, troll from the Pedro Grounds to Cape Chirikoff through mid-June, then work the net through the height of the Alaskan summer, when dusk sits purple on the waters until one in the morning and a fine dawn comes softly at three. Early September was boom time for dog salmon, and in a good year they held until the end of the month; then, depending on how lucky Bob was feeling, or how desperate his need for money was, he either hung around and fished until it was entirely pointless or hung it up and steamed south before the big weather brewed. The middle of October was late for going home.

Some bad things had happened this season. He'd gone through a lot of foul, nasty weather, doubling and even tripling up a lot of three-quarter-inch lines that chafed through inside of a week's time. A good net sunk, the fishing had been poor, and he'd passed a lot of good hours tied to floats. In mid-July his girlfriend of two years took flight. She got off at Port Chilikoot, just south of Haines, and refused to come back on board. They argued outside a house on the old army post with the wind screaming in their faces. Bob was one of life's losers, she said: she had to get on with her life. Then she shut the door to the house, and that was the end of the matter.

The result was that Bob had to find a new deckhand, which he did by steaming up to Skagway. In a tourist saloon he turned up Hutchinson's son, who was nineteen and a half and weighed two hundred pounds: precisely at that juncture in his earthly existence when he would be capable of pushing his body hardest. Bo Pomeroy, who was fifteen years older, knew this exceedingly well. The boy was strong and, more than that, eager – though he exerted himself to couch the adolescent surface of his zeal in an adult's knowingness and ease. He was healthy and well fed. He'd driven north from Seattle in a pickup truck, accompanied by a high-school wrestling buddy who had eventually abandoned him for work on a halibut schooner. He had wanted an adventure on the AlCan Highway, he had wanted to be a reckless knockabout, but of course, Bob knew he was only a kid who would go to college one day, to a state university where a lot of beer got drunk in dormitory rooms and fraternity house hallways. In the meantime, here he was in the Far North.

Bob himself had grown up near Bellingham, in a double-wide mobile home owned by an aunt. He never graduated from high school. He began cutting cedar bolts at fifteen and shipped out for Alaska two years later, while other boys his age were playing baseball.

The *Fearless* left Skagway with her quarters stocked with gear and her fuel tanks topped off with diesel oil. It was a bright, even joyous July day as they manoeuvred past Eldred Rock and Sullivan Island. While his boat made the run down Lynn Canal, Bob tuned the radar and depth sounder, and because the sun was out on a fair afternoon and the green Alaskan waters lay sleek and glassy, and because his new deckhand seemed stalwart and reliable he felt – for the first time since May – good about things.

Bob went outside, made his way forward, and peered up into the pilot-house window, where Paul – he would not forget this – stood tall behind the wheel. The boy nodded at him gravely, as though he had been steering the *Fearless* for many years – a black-haired boy with blue eyes and a clear face – then fixed his youthful gaze once again to the southeast and the promise of the Chatham Strait fishing grounds.

There was a net closure – no net fishing allowed – so for a few days they trolled for silvers. They worked the rip at Point Gardner for a dozen modest fish; they dragged twenty-two fathoms off Admiralty Island for two dozen more. Bob showed Paul how to work the gurdies and how to unsnap the leaders as they came up with their spoons and how to coil them neatly in the stern. The boy learned immediately how to gaff his fish behind the gills so as to avoid damaging the meat. Then came a twenty-four-hour gill-net opening. They fished a tight corner with the Port Protection fleet, the tide running hard, the boats close to one another, the evening westerly tossing spray over the pilothouses. In the dark the boy picked his first net clean – sixty-five good chums in a stiff night wind beneath the season's first northern lights. The moon went down and they fished the beach by radar, running in tight and dropping the net light, then ploughing out again and dropping net off the drum. They drifted through a kelp bed and the boy cleaned out the net, dropping fish in the hold and strands of kelp over the side. Then, with the net set, they revealed themselves.

The boy had spoken about high-school football games and of his painful seasons on the wrestling team. He could play the guitar, he insisted; he had once played the violin, too. He regretted his lack of a greater seriousness when it came to making music. He had smoked marijuana more than a few times but had taken LSD only once – yes, their son had dropped acid, said Bob; it was something he had to tell them. In the course of Paul's acid trip he had put his face beside a beehive without trepidation and had relaxed enough to climb a sheer cliff and had wandered down the fairways of a golf course. He was not sure if he wanted to go to college. He thought perhaps that he would own a health club or open a pizza parlour. Other times, he said, he wanted to be a cop; maybe, then again maybe not. He confessed to confusion about his future and announced that during his time aboard he had come to miss the company of women. He wanted, he said, to be close to somebody, that much he knew.

The next day they struck surf scoters off the water, and the boy remembered duck hunting long ago and the eccentricities of his family's long-dead chocolate Lab, a timid dog named Duke.

In August Paul confronted his first evil weather. They set the net in a heavy rain, a big wind driving seawater across both decks. A gale came up, the tide ebbed hard, and Bob decided to reel up and slip into a bight in the shoreline. But the high speed in the reel drive quit against the tide with two-thirds of the net still in the water. In the storm, with the wind blowing the tops off the waves and the offshore rips boiling in overfalls and combers, the *Fearless* towed her net beyond Cape Lynch, where the tide swept her out to open water. The net-winch clutch quit working after fifteen minutes, so the two of them pulled net by hand. They took turns. They worked in their rain gear with the sea coming from all directions, a maelstrom from which they turned their faces. Darkness came and the sea steepened; the *Fearless* cupped deeply into westerly swells and Bob had to stay behind the wheel. Paul pulled for four hours with the sea bellowing in his ears. It was what he'd come to Alaska for in the first place, Bob knew, what he believed in some deep private corner of his heart. *Tribulation and hardship*. Later Paul admitted to this. He said that his father had trained it into him.

Weather prevented them from making the run south, and for three days they lay at anchor at Twin Coves, holed up and reading novels. Bob brought out his bag of marijuana and they smoked a lot of it. The boy began to speak out of boredom and recollected the high-school girls he'd undressed and fondled and sometimes planked, and then he communicated to Bob a recent revelation: If you liked somebody, the sex was better. If you loved somebody, it was like floating in marmalade clouds heated five degrees above room temperature. If you didn't like somebody, forget everything. This he hadn't known in high school.

Paul explained how he'd stolen on a regular basis whole cases of beer from delivery trucks. Before football games he'd popped little white speed pills, and once he'd snorted cocaine. He'd been hauled in for weaving at high speed down boulevards and his father – did Mr Hutchinson recollect? – had come to the precinct station at three-thirty in the morning to collect him with no small disgust. The boy had puked in his father's Buick. His father had pulled over to the shoulder of the freeway and barked him across the brows. Did Mr Hutchinson remember this incident? Paul with vomit dribbling in strings from his lips and a welt forming between his eyes?

The summer after graduation the boy had gone to the mountains with a friend from the football team. They'd gobbled peyote buttons, and Paul, in the woods, had dreamed of green Alaskan waters. In Alaska, he told Bob, he intended to find himself.

Now, in Alaska, stoned on the deck of Bob's fishing boat, Paul turned enlightened and decided that the key to his existence was not to end up like his father. 'A real macho freak,' he'd said to Bob Pomeroy. 'It's probably too late,' the boy had added.

This was the truth, Bob told Hutchinson. This was how Paul had spoken.

Actually, Paul had professed to be rethinking everything about his existence. Football, for example, and wrestling – he had never enjoyed either one. Why had he done these things anyway? What was the point? Maybe he would study psychology and figure it all out. He had recently, he said, read a psychology book – *On the Development of the Human Personality*, by Dr Anton Friedman. Some of you, the book stated, was just what the sperm and egg decided and a lot of you was what happened before you were two. Some more was between two and thirteen. After that, the book said, you did what you had to do, you were a robot. Bob had read no psychology books and wondered if there couldn't be some path of escape from such a fated, miserable condition. Paul thought that perhaps it was in another psychology book, that there were some people who thought so, yes.

They got more stoned and became unintelligible, even to themselves.

For three days there were sixty-knot winds and twelve-foot seas, and the wipers froze solid and ice formed in the rigging. In a lull they made the run down to Point Horton, but the radar locked up, and they had to jog through a snow squall, making no progress for eleven hours. In Ketchikan they paired up with another boat, the *Wayfarer*, for the run across Dixon Entrance. After two days the southeast gale died down and they lit south, running for home, but ill weather blew hard down from the north, and the two boats soon lay at anchor in Customhouse Cove with snow freezing against the pilothouse windows. Once again the rigging iced up; the radio reported steepening seas and a fifty-five-knot gale. Then, after three days of this, the forecast called for clearing and the skippers of the two boats agreed to run for it.

At three in the morning Bob flicked on the radar and stared for a long time at the empty scope while Paul slept in the fo'c'sle. A rough squall passed through Customhouse Cove, and, in his rain gear, reluctantly, Bob went out to let slip a few more yards of anchor chain. At dawn they pushed off for Foggy Bay with the *Wayfarer* running to port and in radio contact; they cleared Mary Island and ploughed into the vast open just as the Coast Guard broadcast an emergency gale warning for the length of the northern coast. Bob radioed the *Wayfarer*, but since the seas in front of them were apparently calm she radioed back to say they ought to run for Foggy Bay at least. There was time, her skipper said, before the wind came up.

The *Fearless* fell in, quartering to stern, but the wind, a northerly, came in at seven-thirty. The water darkened. The tops of the swells blew off all around so that shreds of foam flew past. The seas grew tall and the two boats jogged in tandem to put their trolling poles down. The last of the flood came at eight-fifteen, and as the tide turned back against the wind the sea rolled even higher. It rolled over both decks of the *Fearless* easily, so that Bob had to send Paul down to pump clear the bilges. At the wheel, Bob negotiated swells out of the west at

30

first, then from the south with the southwest chop and the tide race pushing on top. The waves pressed so hard against the windows that the glass sagged with their weight. Water poured in over the stern, filled the cockpit, then drained as the boat throttled uphill. Once, to port, Bob caught a glimpse of the *Wayfarer*, a third of her keel visible as she rode the waves. Then Paul stood beside him with a strand of vomit hanging from his mouth and an ashen, defeated face.

Bob had passed a few storms at the bilges himself, clearing the pump filters of their detritus, wedged in tight alongside the engine, listening to its scream and breathing the putrid odour of diesel fumes, old salmon, and musty wood. It was not long before a person inevitably had to vomit in that unlit and windowless hellhole. The storm shook the entire length of the boat, and as you lay on your belly her hull shuddered under you, and you prayed with your face to the vomity ribbing that she wouldn't go under while you were down there alone beside that slamming engine.

'You'd better get down there,' Bob said. 'We gotta have you hard pumping bilge.'

'I need air,' the boy said. 'A couple minutes' worth of air.'

He descended anyway, shame-faced, wiping his mouth. Darkness came. The seas steepened further. Water buried the bow to the cabin; they lost radio contact with the *Wayfarer*, but Bob could see her

running lights as she mounted into a
nearby wave, and he was glad of her
presence in that great emptiness. He
kept the *Fearless* diving deep into the
troughs and throttled hard up the
steepest hills of white water, listening
to the engine change pitch. Then, in
the darkness, the mast toppled and
with it the radio antenna. Bob heard
them go, a crash that coincided with a
tremendous shudder throughout the
length of the boat. The *Fearless* listed
to starboard while her mast still hung
on by its rigging.

The boy emerged topside again and
looked fearfully at Bob. For a moment
he seemed about to speak and he
blinked – it was a question.

'Cut it loose,' Bob Pomeroy or-
dered. 'Cut the whole mast right loose.'

The boy blinked. 'Now?' he asked. 'OK.'

Paul went out with a flashlight and a hatchet. It was the last time Bob saw him, alive or dead. He wore his rain gear. He went without question. There was vomit hanging from his lip.

They were swamped by three big ones in succession. They rode low and the engine died. The *Fearless* turned broadside immediately and, helpless now, did a half-roll into the ocean. It seemed to Bob both sudden and inevitable; he had just enough time to drag back the door of the pilothouse and make a grab before the water hit him.

He stayed with the boat, clinging to a gunnel, and called, screamed for Paul. The boy, no doubt, was hung up in the rigging, which now lay submerged beneath the waves. Either that or he'd been swept overboard. Bob went on calling for him anyway.

He called for no more than half a minute. Then he stopped. He adjusted his grip and hung on, silent. The lights of the *Wayfarer* cut through the sleet; she came near, her skipper made some minor adjustments – tricky and deft given the boiling of the waves – and then her deckhand tossed out a life ring. He missed for two or three tries before the *Wayfarer* quartered in closer. Bob hung on. He was getting numb; his hands no longer felt anything. The life ring came his way again. There were two more tries, and then he grabbed it. He let go of the gunnel and held on to the life ring. Then he was under. He came up again. The deckhand pulled him to within ten feet of the pilothouse before a wave pitched Bob on to the *Wayfarer's* after-deck, where he broke his nose against the net winch.

After Bob Pomeroy had gone away – after the dinner and the complicit mourning, after they had falsely healed one another, two men moving toward a tidy farewell – Hutchinson's daughter wept uncontrollably and Hutchinson's wife consoled her. They sat together in a paralysed embrace astride the dining-room table. His daughter blew her nose repeatedly into a napkin, and his wife urged her to indulge herself fully. 'Weep,' she said. 'Let it go, darling.'

In the kitchen Hutchinson meted

out three fingers of bourbon and stood for a long time beside the sink, a hand laid atop his head. The image of his son with the flashlight and the hatchet became more vivid as he stood there. He exerted himself to see this more clearly – the boy in rain gear, saying nothing in the storm, vomit depending from his chin. There are things no father should imagine, he realised.

He sat by himself at the kitchen table. Laura came in bearing a photo album and showed him the portrait he'd taken of Paul with his first slain duck, seven years ago. Then she removed it from its plastic sleeve and passed it into his keeping.

'That little story of yours,' she said. 'Your little Paul-and-his-first-duck story, like he ever wanted to go hunting in the first place. Like he ever *needed* that.'

'I didn't want to be like my father either,' Hutchinson reminded her. 'My father was such a coward, Laura. I responded to that.'

'Don't blame this on your father,' Laura said.

'There's no point in blame,' replied Hutchinson.

'Yes, there is,' said Laura.

He couldn't sit with her. He left. He went upstairs and sat in Paul's bedroom and looked at the boy's collection of sports trophies. He'd started him hunting at eight years old, he recalled; Paul had worn two sweaters. Hutchinson had lit the hand warmer for him, and the boy passed the day sitting on a plastic bag in the blind and pointing whenever ducks went overhead.

Paul squeezed his fingers against his ears whenever the gun went off. His cheeks flushed the hue of apple skins. He chewed on candy bars; traces of them lay against the corners of his lips. For a half-hour he held a dead mallard in his lap, inspecting its legs and feet. He slept going home, then woke and slipped a piece of bubble gum between his teeth. He leaned against the car door, watching the sageland outside his window and humming violin *études*. The boy took violin lessons after school, a thing he seemed to enjoy. But he quit eventually, and Laura blamed Hutchinson.

When Paul was twelve Hutchinson

put a shotgun in his hands. They went out three times, and the boy took his shots without establishing the proper lead. Hutchinson did not desist, however. The boy had fast reflexes and only needed consistent prodding to develop his marksmanship.

It was early in December when the boy got his first kill. They drove in under some power lines at dawn, mallards getting off the little feeder stream before them. They parked and hauled their decoys out, and the boy watched the dark surface of the pond. 'It's all ice,' he said. 'It's iced over.'

'We'll break it out,' answered Hutchinson. 'It's thin enough stuff. We can break it.'

They walked a half-mile, through rushes, to a point of sedge, the boy following Duke, who wagged his tail. Hutchinson kicked out the ice in his waders. 'Come on in here,' he said to Paul. 'Help me out. I need a hand.'

The boy kicked at the ice. It came free in fractured slabs. They set out the decoys in the shape of a V, its point aimed into the wind.

'It's cold,' the boy said. 'My fingers.'

'It's perfect,' answered Hutchinson. 'Some wind. A little weather. It'll be the only pond around with open water.'

'My waders are leaking,' the boy informed him.

They waited for a while in the reeds together. The boy sat beside the dog. Ducks began to move. Hutchinson brought down two stray teal as they winged in low just behind the blind, and Duke ineptly retrieved both of them.

'My feet are frozen,' the boy said.

'I know,' said Hutchinson. 'Mine are frozen, too. Your feet get cold when you go hunting.'

Hutchinson watched a flight of mallards circle. When they began to pull away he called them back; he worked them judiciously. 'OK,' he said to Paul. 'Be ready now. They're turning. They're all yours, son. *Take* them.'

'My hands are frozen,' Paul whined. 'I can't get my safety off.'

'Damn!' said Hutchinson. 'Get ready!'

The boy at last fired three shots, missing all, and reloaded without saying anything.

'You were under them,' explained

Hutchinson. 'Throw your elbow out more. Lead smoothly.'

'My fingers are frozen,' the boy answered.

In the afternoon the weather worsened. A whipping snow fell, and the wind blew harder from the north.

'Let's go,' the boy said. 'I can't feel my feet. I don't *like* going hunting anyway.'

Hutchinson counselled patience. 'Dusk,' he said. 'You'll get good shots at dusk. They won't flare off then. They'll be looking for a place to set.'

'I'm freezing.'

'It doesn't help to talk about it.'

'I can't feel my feet.'

'Me neither,' said Hutchinson. 'Just ignore it.'

The boy fell grimly quiet after this.

He watched the sky with his hands in his pockets, jumping up and down in place, the gun on the ground beside him.

The snow landed on the shoulders of their coats now and settled on their caps and on the decoys. The wind blew it stinging into their faces. Flights of ducks would appear in it suddenly, the whistling of their wings and their cries long preceding them. It was fast shooting, and Hutchinson felt challenged by it. By two-thirty he'd shot his limit.

At three o'clock a single greenhead came winging low across the point of sedge and Paul fired straight-on, and then going-over and finally going-away. On the last shot the duck arced steeply to the ice, where it flopped for a while before settling.

'I hit him,' the boy said. But he didn't seem happy about it, he seemed glum. He looked across the ice at the place where the duck had fallen.

'Congratulations,' said Hutchinson. 'You've gotten started.'

Duke would not venture out on to the ice, so Hutchinson kicked a path directly through it and made the retrieve himself.

They walked back to the truck and ran the heater. Already Hutchinson was inventing the story of it: a long third shot, the steep drop of the lone mallard, the boy too astonished to say anything – too astonished to speak!

Hutchinson, just before dusk, made the boy stand beside the truck tailgate with his first duck clutched in his right fist. He brought his camera up to his face and peered at his son through the viewfinder. 'Smile, damn it,' he said to his son. 'That's your first duck you've got there.'

'I feel bad about killing him,' the boy said.

'I know,' said Hutchinson. 'Smile anyway.'

The boy tried. He'd felt an urge to please, that was clear now. That was too clear. His face contorted this way and that, searching for an appropriate configuration, until at last it arranged itself in the shape of a smile that was the falsest thing Hutchinson had ever seen.

'Come on,' he said. 'You don't look like yourself. Smile naturally, Paul.'

But it didn't happen, and Hutchinson was forced to snap the picture with his son's face arranged in this false way.

Look, said the picture now, *I'm not myself. I only want to please.*

Remorse rolled through Hutchinson with all the force of an ocean wave. He knew that Paul's brief life had, in some measure, been a lie and that his death was Hutchinson's own to contend with; the son's death was on his father's hands.

Hutchinson's daughter was drinking vanilla cream tea and had the television on. It was one in the morning. Rain ricocheted off the windows. His daughter wore no make-up, she'd dropped her shoes on the rug. She was sadly overweight, and it caused him to wonder: what had made it thus? What cords connected to which ancestors? He understood that he didn't know the answer to this question. He was cognisant of his wider ignorance and of the mystery of his daughter. Perhaps he had never known her. Perhaps she was troubled in a private way, or loathed him secretly.

He touched her cheek, and then her chin, and then he kissed the top of her head. 'I'm sorry,' he said. 'I'm so sorry, Cara.'

'Go see Mom,' his daughter answered.

He went to Laura in the bedroom. She was in bed, and she did not turn toward him at first when he sat down at the foot of the mattress. 'My God,' she said. 'I keep thinking of it. Seeing him underwater like that. It's just . . . my God,' she repeated.

'Laura,' he said. 'Please look at me.'

'I can't stand to think of it,' Laura told him. 'All of it, none of it, it's just so – '

She wept.

'Laura,' he said. 'Forgive me.'

'Forgiveness is hard,' his wife whispered hoarsely. 'It isn't in me, you know.'

'You've been right about everything,' explained Hutchinson. 'I'm guilty, guilty, I've – '

She held him then, but with a distant pity, and they were both inconsolable.

'What was it I ever loved in you?' his wife said after a while. 'Why in God's name did I love you?'

'I don't know,' Hutchinson cried. 'How can I answer that?'

But after ten minutes she held him tightly and cradled his head in her hands. He felt, now, that her sadness included him. 'Calm yourself,' she whispered, and Hutchinson was as grateful for that as he had ever been for anything in all of his fifty years. 'Quiet now,' she breathed. 'Peace, peace and quiet.'

That night his erection was powerful, bursting with his sadness. Afterward he cried with his face in her greying hair. They lay side by side looking up at the ceiling. 'What the hell is everything about?' he said. 'None of it makes any sense.'

'You're human,' she replied. 'You're frail.'

He put his head against her belly, in the warm place he had been accustomed to in the days before his son drowned.

A NOTE ON THE AUTHOR

David Guterson is the author of *Snow Falling on Cedars*, a novel, and *The Country Ahead of Us, the Country Behind*, a collection of short stories. He lives in Puget Sound on the west coast of the USA.

ALSO AVAILABLE AS BLOOMSBURY QUIDS

Margaret Atwood	*The Labrador Fiasco*
T. Coraghessan Boyle	*She Wasn't Soft*
Nadine Gordimer	*Harald, Claudia, and their Son Duncan*
Jay McInerney	*The Queen and I*
Candia McWilliam	*Change of Use*
Will Self	*A Story for Europe*
Patrick Süskind	*Maître Mussard's Bequest*
Joanna Trollope	*Faith*
Tobias Wolff	*Two Boys and a Girl*

Jimmy and the Desperate Woman, D. H. Lawrence
Einstein's Dreams, Alan Lightman
Bright Lights, Big City, Jay McInerney
Debatable Land, Candia McWilliam
Bliss and Other Stories, Katherine Mansfield
The Garden Party and Other Stories, Katherine Mansfield
So Far from God, Patrick Marnham
Lies of Silence, Brian Moore
The Lonely Passion of Judith Hearne, Brian Moore
The Pumpkin Eater, Penelope Mortimer
Lives of Girls and Women, Alice Munro
The Country Girls, Edna O'Brien
Coming Through Slaughter, Michael Ondaatje
The English Patient, Michael Ondaatje
In the Skin of a Lion, Michael Ondaatje
Running in the Family, Michael Ondaatje
Let Them Call it Jazz, Jean Rhys
Wide Sargasso Sea, Jean Rhys
Keepers of the House, Lisa St Aubin de Téran
The Quantity Theory of Insanity, Will Self
The Pigeon, Patrick Süskind
The Heather Blazing, Colm Tóibín
Cocktails at Doney's and Other Stories, William Trevor
The Choir, Joanna Trollope
Angel, All Innocence, Fay Weldon
Oranges are not the only fruit, Jeanette Winterson
The Passion, Jeanette Winterson
Sexing the Cherry, Jeanette Winterson
In Pharaoh's Army, Tobias Wolff
This Boy's Life, Tobias Wolff
Orlando, Virginia Woolf
A Room of One's Own, Virginia Woolf

AVAILABLE AS BLOOMSBURY POETRY CLASSICS